Garfield's

Guide
To
PIGGING OUT

JIM DAVIS

RAVETTE PUBLISHING

CRASH

AIM A LITTLE OFF TODAY, GARFIELD?

THIS TASTES LIKE LINOLEUM!

GARFIELD! LOOK AT THAT STOMACH!

YOU MUST TAKE YOUR HEALTH MORE SERIOUSLY

IT'S HARD TO BE SERIOUS WHILE STARING UP YOUR NOSE